Unlocking an Intimate Marriage

A Small Group Discussion Guide for Married Couples

By Dr. Michael Sytsma and Shaunti Feldhahn

This study includes 8 video sessions.

Find them for free at
UnlockinganIntimateMarriage.com

See page page 91 for free access instructions.

Also available through RightNow Media.

This book is designed as a participant guide for those working through the *Unlocking an Intimate Marriage* small group video study. This video study is designed to give general guidance to facilitate intimacy. It is not designed to provide clinical advice or specific direction to any individual couple. Not all guidance suggested in this book or study will work for all marriages or individuals. Seek professional assistance if any suggestion in this work causes distress.

Published by: Sexualis Veritas Press, LLC, Suwanee, GA.

https://SexualisVeritasPress.com

Second Edition

Previous edition published by Sexual Wholeness Resources LLC is identical except cover, ISBN, and publisher.

.

ISBN: 979-8-9902940-0-4 (Paperback)

ISBN: 979-8-9902940-1-1 (eBook)

Cover and interior design by: Cynthia Bradford

We would like to thank RightNow Media
and an anonymous donor
for their partnership in making this study possible.

Table of Contents

About the Authors

Michael Sytsma, PhD, is a Licensed Professional Counselor, Certified Sex Therapist, Ordained Minister, professor, and national speaker. He has over 30 years of clinical experience in sex therapy and is the founder of Building Intimate Marriages, Inc. and co-founder of Sexual Wholeness, Inc. He is a professor at 5 different seminaries and graduate schools and regular trainer at professional conferences. He is co-author of *Secrets of Sex & Marriage, 8 Surprises that Make all the Difference*, with Shaunti Feldhahn and contributor to several other works.

Find out more about Dr. Sytsma and his ministry at IntimateMarriage.org

Shaunti Feldhahn is a social researcher and best-selling author who investigates the little things that make a big difference in life and relationships. Her books, such as *For Women Only* and *For Men Only*, have sold more than three million copies in 26 languages. With a graduate degree from Harvard University, she was an analyst on Wall Street and today applies her analytical skills to investigating eye-opening, life-changing truths that help people thrive. Shaunti (often with her husband, Jeff) speaks at dozens of events a year around the world.

Find out more about Shaunti at Shaunti.com or SurprisingHope.com.

We would love your feedback.

As you work through this study, we invite you to jump over to our anonymous form and let us know about your experience with the material. We greatly value it.

https://UnlockinganIntimateMarriage.com/feedback

Before You Begin

What is this study about, and what is the process?

You want a thriving, intimate marriage.

We want to help you get there.

The study you are about to embark on has literally been decades in development. As an experienced therapist with a specialty in marriage and sex therapy, and as a pastor and professor at multiple seminaries, Michael Sytsma has spent the last thirty-five years working with couples just like you, and training others to do the same. And for the last few of those years, he and researcher and best-selling author Shaunti Feldhahn conducted a nationally-representative study of thousands of men and women in order to uncover some vital truths that will help you build the close, intimate, thriving marriage you are looking for.

We — Michael and Shaunti — are creating this small group study based on key findings from that research, as well as from Shaunti's many other marriage-related research studies and books, Michael's clinical experience, and the best practices of many other counselors, pastors, and therapists.

We will be helping you consider and discuss vital marriage matters like how to revive or strengthen your feelings of love for each other, how to communicate more effectively, how to navigate each other's secret insecurities and hot buttons, and how to be on each other's team. We will carefully open the door to sensitive topics like your different approaches to physical intimacy, understanding and navigating intimate connection that engages the heart, and ways to create true oneness in your marriage.

Which leads to a crucial point. Our recent research study resulted in our book, *Secrets of Sex & Marriage,* which is a companion book to this course. Yet as you can see, like the book, this small group study is not only about sex. However, many of the topics may also have an application in your intimate life. Part 1 of this study will be more focused on marriage overall, and will include elements of that application. Part 2 will be more specific and dial in on several simple but valuable topics that can either help or hinder your intimate life.

Although some of these topics are sensitive, there is great value in sharing encouragement with other couples on the journey. We want this to be a fun and valuable experience, not a cringey one. Thus, the "As a Group" sections are designed specifically to address all topics in a comfortable, practical, but general way during your small group. To make that work, we encourage all participants to read and honor the "Creating a safe space for group discussion" guidelines. The "Bringing it Home" sections will allow the two of you to privately discuss your personal application at other times.

Key tip for couples: weekly "working date"

As you work toward growing as a couple, the most impactful exercise I (Michael) see couples implement is a weekly "working date."

When consistent, these "business meetings for your marriage" transform marriages rather quickly. You can learn more on the instruction sheet available at IntimateMarriage.org/workingdate.

We highly recommend that you begin this habit if it is not already part of your practice as a couple. You will need to set aside time each week for the "Bringing it Home" section of this study anyway, so this becomes a great opportunity to start.

Accessing the videos

Access to the videos comes with the purchase of this workbook. You can access the videos directly in two ways.

1. Through our website: UnlockinganIntimateMarriage.com/
   See page page 91 for free access instructions.
1. Through RightNow Media.

We would like to thank RightNow Media and an anonymous donor for their partnership in making this study possible.

About the unique schedule

Each of the eight sessions has three teaching segments. You will watch a four- to five-minute video clip, have a small-group discussion about it, then return for the next short video clip and so on. At the end, the short **Bringing it Home** video sends couples home to discuss and apply what they have learned. This format allows the leader and group to quickly "get back on topic" if conversation wanders into territory that is off topic or not comfortable for some in the group. Each session has roughly fifteen minutes of video, total.

To allow plenty of time for group discussion, we recommend 90 minutes for this process. If your group has a tight schedule, you can complete all videos and discussions within 60 minutes by allowing 10-15 minutes for each of the three group discussions (focusing especially on any questions marked "Important" (labeled by this graphic ❶ in the workbook). You may also want to omit the Review section, and the Optional questions (marked by this graphic ❸).

Whatever your time frame is, keep an eye on the clock during group discussions so you come back on time to watch and discuss the next video.

Bible study

Principles and passages from the Bible are woven throughout all eight sessions of this study. For those who want to go deeper into the biblical discussion, we have created a special "Deeper Into the Word" section of this workbook on pagepage 77.

In any initiative or study that involves learning and growing on a particular topic, it is easy to get stuck in a focus on that topic and forget to raise our eyes to the bigger, eternal picture. So as we work on building intimacy in our marriages, the deeper Bible study section will help us even more purposefully focus on our relationship with God. The goal is to keep always before our minds how to glorify and follow Him in the midst of our day-to-day efforts in our marriage.

This Bible study section is a companion to the existing discussion within each of the eight sessions. You will see directions to discuss certain verses and questions after specific video teaching segments. Note that the expanded Bible study questions *build* on the regular questions (including the scriptural questions) rather than replacing them. Another option is to use the Bible study section as a supplemental personal or couples' study during the time between sessions.

Creating a safe space for group discussion

A thriving, intimate marriage is an almost universal desire, but tackling the subject in a marriage group can take courage. We are glad you have taken these first steps to explore this material. We want this to be a great experience for everyone – which requires everyone to have the same expectation for how to handle any sensitive discussions. For example, for years I (Michael) avoided requests to write any small-group material on sex and intimacy. It is a powerful topic. But the Church is the one place where it should be safe to talk about a subject God paid a good deal of attention to. So after many years working on this, I believe we have a format that helps this material to be safer. Thus, here are some guidelines that will help everyone discuss the sensitive topics we are guiding you through:

- Remember, everyone has a different level of comfort with sensitive topics. Please be gentle with those who are more conservative in their comfort level. There may be a very good reason they are more private. (For example, depending upon who you read, about one in three women and one in five men have experienced some form of sexual trauma or abuse.)
- Discuss as a couple if there are any particular boundaries you would like maintained as you discuss and work through this material in front of others. Then be diligent about honoring those boundaries.
- Honor your spouse in public, and be careful to never expose them in front of the group. ("Well a date night sounds great, but my spouse will never do that because he/she is so cheap!") That is never okay, and does not improve marital intimacy. It is human to want to have others validate you as reasonable or right, but seeking to get people "on your side" does not validate or honor your spouse. If you try to leverage group opinion to motivate your spouse, it is likely to backfire and make your spouse avoid participating in the group at all. It may even damage the group itself. Exposing your spouse is also likely to cause damage to your marriage. So if you have a very real complaint about your spouse, discuss it with a trusted advisor or counselor, never in public.

- Honor one another, by being willing to work to keep discussions healthy. For example, if someone isn't honoring their spouse, call a flag on the play. Gently let them know what they are saying doesn't feel honoring.
- Also, honor yourself. Don't overexpose or overshare. This is not a therapy group or a support group. We are primarily here to learn together.
- **!** Don't stray off topic. There are land mines just off the path.
- Our design for the four short video and discussion sections will help you facilitate a safe space. If a discussion topic gets uncomfortable, flag the leader. The group can easily move on to the next video clip and shift out of a discussion that is entering into unsafe territory.

Finally, in creating this material, we acknowledge there will be those who use it to seek their own selfish goals and hurt others. ***Please don't be that person***. Commit to being one who keeps the discussion healthy instead. We do believe an open discussion of these concepts, while honoring specific boundaries, can do great good.

A note about sexual topics, in particular

In a culture that is highly sexualized, the culture of Christianity does not always reflect the heart of God on sex and sexuality. It is vital for the church to be a place for open conversations and discussion on this topic in order to advance a healthy biblical view.

Yet there is also a good reason why sex is often a hush-hush subject – especially in faith circles. Sex is a sacred subject with great power. To expand on a metaphor from Christian philosopher Frederick Buechner[1], sex is like nitroglycerin — depending on how it is used, it can blow up mountains, tunnel out connecting paths, or heal the human heart. God's Word encourages us to keep it within the boundaries of marriage to keep it pure.

> *"Drink water from your own cistern,*
> *running water from your own well.*
> *Should your springs overflow in the streets,*
> *your streams of water in the public squares?*
> *Let them be yours alone,*
> *never to be shared with strangers."*
> *-Proverbs 5:15-17*

> *"Marriage should be honored by all,*
> *and the marriage bed kept pure..."*
> *-Hebrews 13:4*

This also includes keeping an intimate *discussion* about sex within the boundaries of marriage as well. Much of the information about our sexuality is private and reserved only for our spouse. So in this study, we have worked hard to ensure that *all* small-group discussion questions about this topic are general and helpful, but not personal. We encourage you to honor your spouse and *not* share intimate details about this sacred part of your life outside of your marriage.

That said, we know that even within our marriages – sometimes *especially* within our marriages – sex can be difficult to talk about. Thus, we hope that this small group study not only opens up an important, general conversation in the church, but that it also becomes a catalyst for you and your spouse to be able to talk well about sexual intimacy – and about the many other aspects of marriage we will cover together.

---

[1] Buechner, F. (1993). *Wishful Thinking*. United Kingdom: HarperCollins.

Our goals for you

Finally, before we begin, let's be clear about what we want to accomplish before the end. This study will be helpful if you learn something about building intimacy and engage in community while you sort through the general concepts. But this study will be a true success if you and your spouse can discuss the application of these concepts at home. Communicating effectively on these topics is what will ultimately lead to you unlocking intimacy in your marriage for a lifetime.

So our goals for you are:

- **To learn and apply key factors to creating intimacy in your marriage;**
- **To grow in community;**
- **To explore God's design for sexual intimacy in marriage;**
- **To build intimate communication with your spouse that will last long after the study is done.**

Enjoy the journey!

PART ONE

Keys to Building an Intimate Marriage

This study is broken into two parts of four lessons each. We're asking you to commit to the first four sessions. At the end of that time, you can choose to stop, or make a commitment to the last four sessions.

The material in this study is designed to develop an intimate marriage, both emotionally and physically. Just as healthy communication is a component of an intimate marriage, a rich sexual relationship is both a reflection of healthy marital intimacy, and a great way to build it. We have designed this study to help your marriage grow from both sides of this equation.

Before you meet with your small group for the first time, please watch the short, pre-session video called "Before you begin." That video includes essential information for every participant. You can view this video through RightNow Media or through the link below.

UnlockinganIntimateMarriage.com/begin

Reclaim Your First Love

Key #1

Welcome to Session 1

Welcome to the first lesson in the Unlocking an Intimate Marriage small group study. Before you begin we encourage you to take these steps:

1. Carefully read through the Before You Begin sections above, especially Creating a safe space for group discussion.
2. Watch the "Before you begin" video.
3. As advised in both resources, be sure to discuss with your spouse if either of you have any particular boundaries you want to be maintained during the small group discussion.

As you go, keep this in mind: This study will be very helpful if you learn some practical, transformational knowledge and engage in community while doing so. It will be a true success if you and your spouse are also able to bring the conversation home and discuss how it applies to the two of *you.*

VIDEO 1.1 GETTING STARTED

notes

Remember, Repent, and Do Examples

Many years ago I (Michael) presented the "remember, repent and do" talk to a group of couples at a ski lodge. At the end of the talk, the couples left to their rooms for the evening. One of the couples approached me the next day and said that as they were leaving, they noticed an old video arcade in the retreat center. "We fell in love and spent a lot of our early dating in a video arcade," he said. "We haven't been in one since before our wedding."

"We looked at each other, bought a fistful of tokens, and started to play. Ninety minutes later, and a lot more quarters than I remember it ever being, we were laughing, flirting, picking on each other, and remembering why we fell in love with each other. It seems kind of crazy, but it worked."

Going back and recreating some of the environment that was present when we fell in love with each other is valuable. We could even say it's one of God's personal recipes.

Here are some of the more generic "Remember, Repent, and Do" examples from many couples:

- Meaningfully saying "I Love You" more.
- Lots of non-sexual caring touches.
- Surprising each other with small thoughtful gifts.
- Long connecting conversations
- Talking about ideas and dreams.
- Bike rides.
- Hiking/bicycling/kayaking
- Going back to walking the dog together.
- Running errands just to be together.
- Game nights with friends
- Making dinners together
- LOTS of emails/texts
- Actively planning when to be together
- Running errands together
- Holding hands everywhere

Discussion:

Share your names, how long you have been married, if you have kids, what you do for living, and one quick story about you as a couple. Possibilities include:

- The story of how you met
- Your craziest date
- Your favorite trip together
- A fun story that illustrates your personalities at play

Leadership note: As noted in the "Before you Begin" video instruction and workbook section, a group with a tight schedule can complete all videos and discussions within 60 minutes if you allow 10-15 minutes for each of the three group discussions. If your group has more time, adjust as needed. Whatever your time frame is, keep an eye on the clock so you come back on time to watch and discuss the second video, and so on from there.

VIDEO 1.2 REMEMBER, REPENT, DO

notes

*"The passion of love bursting into flame
is more powerful than death,
stronger than the grave.
Love cannot be drowned by oceans or floods.
It cannot be bought—
any offer would be scorned
no matter how great."*
                                        - Song of Solomon 8:6b-7 CEV

"I know that you have persevered and endured hardships for the sake of my name, and you have not grown weary. But I have this against you: You have abandoned the love you had at first. Remember then how far you have fallen; repent, and do the works you did at first. Otherwise, I will come to you and remove your lampstand from its place, unless you repent."
-Revelation 2:3-5 (HCSB)

Discussion:

Depending upon the size of your group, it could be fun to listen to everyone's stories, but that amount of time may make this approach to the exercise impractical. Consider breaking into smaller groups of couples to facilitate the process.

- ⊕ How did you meet? What attracted you to your spouse when you first met or in early dating?
- ⊕ What did you "do" together in those early days that provided an environment that helped you fall in love?
- ⊕ What beliefs or attitudes did you have for each other then?
- ⊕ How did those help you fall in love with one another?

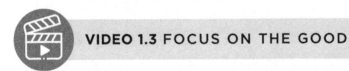

VIDEO 1.3 FOCUS ON THE GOOD

notes

Discussion:

❶ Of all the men/women in the world, you chose to devote your life to your spouse. Tell the group what you found particularly attractive when you first met your spouse. What was the focal point that drew you in and blocked out all others?

❷ Think about the people in your family of origin. Are there characteristics of any of those individuals that you find particularly irksome and tend to focus in on? What is it that leads to focusing on the negative things – the scratches on the porch column, so to speak?

❸ How can we "zoom out" and focus on the positive things instead? What does it take to see the positive in that same member of your family of origin?

 VIDEO 1.4 BRINGING IT HOME

notes

BRINGING IT HOME

As you know, connecting on these topics at home is a crucial part of this study. Please set aside an uninterrupted time to do so (no devices or kids) before the next group session. Growth and change will come from taking what you learn in the group, and discussing and applying it in your marriage.

- Set aside some individual time to really focus on the "remember." Think back to the time you were falling in love, and write down the answers to these questions:
  1. What drew you to your spouse?
  2. What did you do together during the "falling in love" time?
  3. How did you behave toward your spouse?

- Next, schedule a time to talk with your spouse. Begin by asking them what *they* remember. Don't correct or criticize their memory. They are telling a story that has important meaning to them, even if the details of their memory don't match yours. Listen for what is important to them.

- After they have shared, tell your spouse what you remember from your early relationship.

- Consider and discuss: Do you need to "repent," to "turn around" and go back to any of the "first love" attitudes and behaviors?

- As a couple, "do" at least one thing you used to do when you were falling in love.

If you are willing, you will tell the story of what you "did" in the next group.

Other Resources

You might want to view one of the videos available online at theinvisiblegorilla.com. Or search "selective attention" on a video site.

Keep Communication Patterns Clear

Key #2

The most common problem couples identify as the reason they are seeking counseling is communication. Communication is like the oxygen in a marriage relationship.

As you go through this session, remember: This study will be very helpful if you learn some practical, transformational knowledge and engage in community while doing so. It will be a true success if you and your spouse are also able to bring the conversation home and discuss how it applies to the two of you.

Review:

Our goal for this study is to help unlock intimacy in your marriage. Last session we focused on remembering our early relationship and rekindling the early desire we had to be with each other. Who was it we fell in love with and how did we accomplish the task of fostering love for each other?

As a group, take five minutes to share if, in the course of *Remember*, *Repent*, and *Do*, you <u>did</u> something as a couple since the last meeting that was reminiscent of your early relationship. Did it help you remember the individual you chose?

VIDEO 2.1 THE ANSWER REALLY IS "COMMUNICATION."

notes

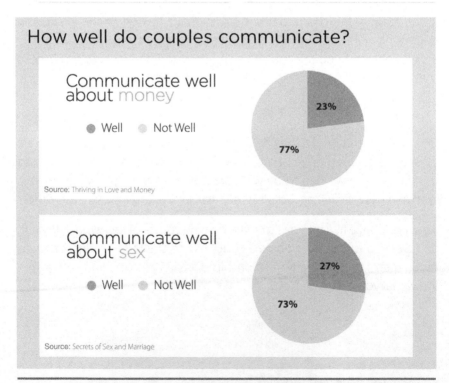

How well do couples communicate?

Communicate well about money

● Well ○ Not Well

23%

77%

Source: Thriving in Love and Money

Communicate well about sex

● Well ○ Not Well

27%

73%

Source: Secrets of Sex and Marriage

Discussion:

⊕ What do you believe is God's primary message to us? In other words, if He could communicate only ONE message to us what would that be? How did he seek to communicate that message?

❶ If you could communicate ONLY ONE positive message to your spouse, knowing they would be able to fully hear and integrate it, what would it be?

⊕ How effectively do you believe you currently communicate that message in day-to-day life? How do you send counter messages? (NOTE: You may only speak for yourself. You and your spouse may not necessarily agree with one other about how well each of you communicate, so allow your spouse to assess their own pattern without contradicting them. And take care not to dishonor your spouse in the group.)

 VIDEO 2.2 HOW EFFECTIVELY DO WE COMMUNICATE?

notes

Communication traps and fixes

"We cannot not communicate" is an axiom of communication articulated by Paul Watzlawick (look him up on Wikipedia). He pointed out that all interaction is communication; both verbal and non-verbal feedback says something to the other person.

Spouses often complain that they aren't communicating, but an observer would be able to see that they are communicating just fine. They just don't like what the other is saying. Or they may be sending mixed messages or unclear messages.

Many researchers have pointed out the blocks to effective communication. In their book *Fighting for Your Marriage*, noted marriage researchers Howard Markman and Scott Stanley point out four "danger signs" in couple communication:

1. **Escalation** – getting louder or otherwise trying to overpower the conversation.
2. **Invalidation** – sending the message that what you think is wrong, stupid, or otherwise not as good as what I think.
3. **Negative interpretation** – if there are two ways to interpret what you are saying or doing, I choose the one that is least favorable about you.
4. **Withdrawal and Avoidance** – shutting down, pulling away, or steering clear of the issue altogether.

Though we all use each of these at times, we tend to have a primary "go-to tactic" and a backup when our usual tactic isn't working. Knowing how we tend to short-circuit effective communication can help us interrupt unhealthy cycles.

Drs Markman and Stanley (with colleagues) developed the Prevention and Relationship Education Program (PREP) to teach what they learned in their research. PREP is one of the most researched and respected programs in the marriage field. PREP teaches the danger signs as well as interventions — including the speaker/listener technique — that largely prevents couples from engaging in these danger signs.

Couples can work through the program at **LoveTakesLearning.com**.

To learn how these principles integrate within a Christian framework, pick up a copy of the book, *A Lasting Promise* by Scott M. Stanley, Daniel Trathen, Savanna McCain, and B. Milton Bryan.

Discussion:

- Rate yourself on a scale of 1-10 and explain your answer:
  - How well did you listen to your parents?
  - How well do you listen at work?
  - How well do you listen to your spouse?
- When someone isn't listening to you, what is your typical tactic for getting them to hear you? (e.g., I get louder, I overwhelm them with facts, I appeal to their emotions, I give up, I repeat myself in a different way, etc.) How well does your tactic generally work?
- Consider the principle that you can't not communicate. Share an example of a way you communicate that you might not be aware of in the moment (in your marriage, at your job, with friends, with family…). Remember not to dishonor others in sharing about yourself.

 VIDEO 2.3 FOCUS ON THE GOOD

notes

Discussion:

❶ We presumably know that our spouse has tender places inside. So why might we communicate in a way that hits those nerves, rather than building our spouse up? What can or should we do about it, if anything?

❷ As you consider your own inner insecurities, give an example of words or actions that really "speak life" to your heart, even if they might look like a minor thing to someone else.

❸ What do you think about the idea of keeping our spouse's insecurities in mind as we communicate? Is that "enabling" weaknesses in our spouse? Caring for our spouse well? Both?

Listening Levels:

Entry-level listening: You sit quietly and listen attentively to what your spouse is saying the entire time. Refrain from any facial expressions that communicate you disagree. Attend to and absorb what they are saying, rather than allowing yourself to begin thinking about your internal edits, comments, or disagreements, or how you want to reply.

Intermediate-level listening: Do the same as the entry-level exercise, but ask your spouse to pause after one or two sentences. Play mirror and "reflect" the content of what they are saying: "So what I hear you saying is …." You may NOT add your opinions, thoughts, observations, or corrections. Just tell them what you heard them say. After that "reflection," allow your spouse to correct you if you didn't quite get it right and, if necessary, you try to "reflect" again. Once you have reflected what they said accurately, they move on to the next couple of sentences.

Advanced-level listening: Do the intermediate level but add feelings into your reflection. "So, what I hear you saying is…, and that makes you feel…." Again, allow them to state how accurate your reflection is, and try it again if you didn't quite get it right.

notes

 BRINGING IT HOME

As you know, connecting on these topics at home is a crucial part of this study. Please set aside an uninterrupted time to do so (no devices or kids) before the next group session. Growth and change will come from taking what you learn in the group, and discussing and applying it in *your* marriage.

Invite your spouse to join you in this application exercise.

1. Pick a "listening level" you want to try (as described in the video and summarized on page "Listening Levels:" on page 22): entry level, intermediate, or advanced. Set a timer for 5 minutes and let them say whatever they would like. You may *not* give your opinion in any way, or correct, challenge, or contradict anything they say. This is *their* story.

2. After the timer goes off, take a minimum of one hour to do something by yourself and consider what you have heard. Seek to truly understand *their* perspective rather than develop ways to convince them your perspective is right. The goal of listening well is to understand. You don't need to agree, but try to see the issue as they do. Then, ask if they are interested in hearing your opinion and discussing what you heard. If so, you can discuss it (and share your opinion) at that point.

Other Resources

- We recommend that couples who want to improve communication work through the PREP communication program online at LoveTakesLearning.com.
- To learn how these communication principles integrate within a Christian framework, pick up a copy of the book, *A Lasting Promise* by Scott M. Stanley, Daniel Trathen, Savanna McCain, and B. Milton Bryan.
- To further investigate the inner lives of men and women, see Shaunti and Jeff Feldhahn's books *For Women Only* and *For Men Only,* as well as the *For Couples Only* video study.
- We speak to the importance of spouses communicating around sexual issues, and some of the research behind it, in the last part of Chapter 2 of *Secrets of Sex and Marriage.*

Grow Your Heart Attitudes

Key #3

Just as certain factors are essential for building a solid foundation for a house, certain factors are essential for building a solid foundation for marital intimacy. The most important factor, of course, is putting God at the center of our marriage. And with God's help, we can then build another essential part of our marriage foundation – the heart attitudes of curiosity, acceptance, and grace.

As you go through this session, remember: This study will be very helpful if you learn some practical, transformational knowledge and engage in community while doing so. It will be a true success if you and your spouse are also able to bring the conversation home and discuss how it applies to the two of you.

Review:

Last session, we demonstrated the importance of building communication skills – and how **all** our interactions are a type of communication. In particular, we discussed how communication will work best, be so much easier, and provide the setting for intimacy once we build the skill of **listening**.

Did you try the homework? As a group, take five minutes to share your experience. What was it like? How successful were you in not giving your opinion while your spouse was talking?

VIDEO 3.1 CURIOSITY

notes

Discussion:

- We all have curiosity about **something.** What are you naturally curious about? (For example, if your hobby is storm chasing, that might signal you have a natural wonder and fascination with how the weather works.)

- On a 1-5 scale (1=not at all curious to 5=totally curious), how curious were you about your spouse when you were dating? Where would you score yourself today in being curious about your spouse? Where would your spouse score you?

- Where do you struggle most with being curious about your spouse's thoughts/opinions/feelings? (Finances, parenting, work, sex, spiritual issues…?) Remember to stay honoring to your spouse.

- What can you do to increase that sense of wonder and fascination with your spouse?

Steps of Acceptance

(From Chapter 9, "Love the One You're With" in Secrets of Sex & Marriage)

Step #1: Realize that change is up to you.

We can only change ourselves. If our spouse must change before we are okay, we are trapped by whether they are willing to change. How can we *not* develop a resentment toward them?

Step #2: Grieve what is not the way you wished

Grief is a powerful acceptance tool. It means truly accepting that something will never be the way we want it to be.[1] Once we grieve who our spouse is not, we are freed to see them for who they are.

Step #3: Extend grace

In a lifelong marriage, grace must be a lifelong choice.

Step #4: Honor them

Focusing on and celebrating the beauty of who they are – despite the areas you see as flaws.

---

[1] Remembering, of course, that some behaviors should never be accepted. See Chapter 9 of *Secrets of Sex & Marriage* for more detail.

 VIDEO 3.2 ACCEPTANCE

notes

"Therefore, accept each other just as Christ has accepted you
so that God will be given glory."

Romans 15:7

Discussion:

As you discuss acceptance, focus on what others need to accept about you rather than what you find frustrating in others. That will help ensure you honor your spouse in this process.

- ❸ What did Paul mean when he wrote to the church in Rome that we are to accept one other as Christ accepted us? Does that mean we accept *everything*?
- ❶ What do you ask others to accept in you? What do you ask your spouse to accept in you that might be difficult for your spouse to accept?
- ❸ How well do you do with the type of grieving and accepting that we have been discussing – especially in grieving what you might want from others, such as from your parents or one of your children?

 VIDEO 3.3 GRACE

notes

"We are made right with God by placing our faith in Jesus Christ. And this is true for everyone who believes, no matter who we are.

For everyone has sinned; we all fall short of God's glorious standard. Yet God, in his grace, freely makes us right in his sight. He did this through Christ Jesus when he freed us from the penalty for our sins."

-Romans 3:22-24

What Is Grace?

The word translated "grace" in the New Testament is the Greek word χαρις, or "charis" in English. Thayer's Greek Lexicon defines grace as: "that which affords joy, pleasure, delight, sweetness, charm, loveliness: grace of speech."[1] The most common definition popularly given is probably "extending unmerited favor".

Presuppositions

In exploring grace and encouraging it to be expressed in relationships, we presume:

- The LORD is a God of grace - Ephesians 2:4-10
- We are called to be Christlike
- Grace is a healing and restorative force
- Our expression of grace has healing and restorative powers

We show grace in a variety of ways, including:

- Focusing on the positive in our spouse
- Choosing to believe the best in them
- Celebrating them being them
- Maintaining a spirit of ongoing forgiveness

For more on the role of grace in marriage, check out Dr. Sytsma's talk *"Grace in Healing and Growing Marital Intimacy"* which is available at: IntimateMarriage.org/grace.

---

[1]Thayer, J. H. (1889). In *A Greek-English lexicon of the New Testament: being Grimm's Wilke's Clavis Novi Testamenti* (p. 665). Harper & Brothers.

Discussion:

- Who would you say has been the most gracious person in your life? Give a specific example of how they extended grace to you.
- Think of an area where you struggle to extend grace to your spouse. (Share this with the group only if doing so would be honoring to your spouse.) How would your marriage be different if you extended a heart of grace in this arena?

 VIDEO 3.4 BRINGING IT HOME

notes

The Power of Curiosity

Each of these heart attitudes is valuable in marriage, but curiosity may be core to a marriage truly becoming intimate.

A valuable change happens as we shift from all the ways we try to get our spouse to be who we want them to be (pestering, ridiculing, guilting, demanding, punishing, etc.) to a position of curiosity where we are seeking to *understand* them instead. Curiosity opens space for true intimacy.

This is particularly true in the arena of sexual intimacy. Being convinced that we know how our spouse "should" be can deeply wound physical intimacy. Being curious about how they *are* can help it thrive.

"Always be full of joy in the Lord. I say it again - rejoice! Let everyone see that you are considerate in all you do. ... Don't worry about anything; instead, pray about everything. Tell God what you need, and thank him for all he has done. Then you will experience God's peace, which exceeds anything we can understand. His peace will guard your hearts and minds as you live in Christ Jesus.

And now, dear brothers and sisters, one final thing. Fix your thoughts on what is true, and honorable, and right, and pure, and lovely, and admirable. Think about things that are excellent and worthy of praise."

-Philippians 4:4-8

 ## BRINGING IT HOME

As you know, connecting on these topics at home is a crucial part of this study. Please set aside an uninterrupted time to do so (no devices or kids) before the next group session. Growth and change will come from taking what you learn in the group, and discussing and applying it in **your** marriage.

In this particular conversation, it is important to be honest but also careful with your spouse's tender feelings.

- ☉ Start a list, and begin by identifying five things that are true, honorable, right, pure, lovely, admirable, excellent and worthy of praise about your spouse. Share those with your spouse before you go on to the next question. For the next few days, keep a running list whenever something new occurs to you.

- ☉ Name one thing about yourself that you think your spouse probably wishes was different. Then discuss this with them. Can you allow it to be an area of grief for them, rather than implying they shouldn't want it to be different? Can you be okay with allowing them to grieve without being negative about them – or yourself?

❸ How well have you grieved who your spouse is not? (Remember to be honoring of your spouse, even in a private space where others aren't listening. You do NOT need to share explicit examples if you suspect that they will overly wound your spouse.)

❸ On a day-to-day practical basis, what might each of you do differently in order to ensure you focus more on things that are "worthy of praise" rather than those areas where you need to move toward acceptance?

❸ Before the next group session, share your running "worthy of praise" list with your spouse.

notes

Other Resources

For help learning and applying curiosity, acceptance and grace in your marriage:

- Curiosity - Chapter 7, Secrets of Sex & Marriage.
- Acceptance - Chapter 9, Secrets of Sex & Marriage.
- Grace - IntimateMarriage.org/grace

Build a Shared Vision

Key #4

In this session we will focus on the importance of building a shared vision and sense of oneness as a couple. Many married couples have never really considered how to become *one.* Discussing and creating a shared vision – who they want to become as a couple – is an important part of developing that unity as a husband and wife. *Not* having a shared vision, by contrast, is one reason why some relationships feel rudderless. But once you both know what you are both working toward, where you are trying to head, you are more likely to actually build the marriage you long for.

As you go through this session, remember: This study will be very helpful if you learn some practical, transformational knowledge and engage in community while doing so. It will be a true success if you and your spouse are also able to bring the conversation home and discuss how it applies to the two of *you.*

Review:

If we want a truly intimate marriage, it is important that we work to be the best version of ourselves we can be as we relate to our spouse. During the last session we focused on being curious, accepting, and gracious.

As a group, take five minutes to share whether you completed the **Bringing it Home** exercises. How did it go? (Without sharing details.)

What did you learn?

VIDEO 4.1 MOVE BEYOND PARALLEL PLAY

notes

Discussion:

- How important do you think vision is for an organization? Why?
- Are there areas where parallel play works in an organization? Are there times when parallel play works in marriage?
- Do you believe most couples have a shared vision for most areas of their marriage? For couples that do, what do you think is crucial for getting there?

VIDEO 4.2 PURSUE ONENESS

notes

Then the Lord God said, "It is not good for the man to be alone. I will make a helper who is just right for him." …

"At last!" the man exclaimed. "This one is bone from my bone, and flesh from my flesh! She will be called 'woman,' because she was taken from 'man.'"

This explains why a man leaves his father and mother and is joined to his wife, and the two are united into one.
-Genesis 2:18, 23-24

"Now Adam knew Eve his wife, and she conceived and bore Cain, saying, 'I have gotten a man with the help of the LORD.'"
- Genesis 4:1 (ESV)

"I am praying not only for these disciples but also for all who will ever believe in me through their message. I pray that they will all be one, just as you and I are one—as you are in me, Father, and I am in you. And may they be in us so that the world will believe you sent me. I have given them the glory you gave me, so they may be one as we are one. I am in them and you are in me. May they experience such perfect unity that the world will know that you sent me and that you love them as much as you love me."
- John 17:20-23

Discussion:

🕐 Read Christ's prayer before his crucifixion in John 17:19-23. Jesus asked that we, His followers, be one as He and the Father are one. What does that mean?

❶ How well do you believe Christians pursue oneness and intimacy with each other? What are the reasons why we do or don't do that well? What lessons can we learn from that for marriage?

🕐 What would change in our culture if "oneness," and truly, deeply, interactively knowing one another was seen as the ultimate goal of sex?

VIDEO 4.3 STAY INCARNATE: CARE FOR BOTH BODY AND SPIRIT

notes

_____

_____

_____

_____

_____

_____

_____

Discussion:

- What does it mean to you that Christ was incarnate? What are some ways He exhibited his spiritual nature (God-ness) that are important to you (e.g., being sinless, forgiving sin)? What are some ways He exhibited his physical nature (man-ness) that are important to you (e.g., experiencing hunger, grieving)?

- If we use worship as an analogy, how would we keep worship of God incarnate? How would we make sure we worship God with our body (physical)? How would we make sure we worship God with our spirit?

- Using sex as an example, can you think of examples in culture (Christian culture or world culture) where we see sex as unbalanced to either side – over-focused on the physical or over-focused on the spiritual?

notes

Purpose and vision in the bedroom

Business gurus regularly talk about the intersection of vision and purpose. It is often helpful to explore purpose in defining vision.

So... what do you think the "purpose" is for sexual connection?

There are a host of ideas on that question. Historically, the church often taught that it was all about procreation (sometimes exclusively so). While few still teach this today, others teach it is about bonding (focusing on the potential for biochemical bonding), connection, or oneness. Others focus more on playfulness, pleasure, or even biological imperative.

What you and your spouse believe is the purpose for sex will help you shape your vision for sexual intimacy in your marriage. It may be helpful to explore what each other believes and if the purpose can be different for different encounters.

BRINGING IT HOME

As you know, connecting on these topics at home is a crucial part of this study. Please set aside an uninterrupted time to do so (no devices or kids) before the next group session. Growth and change will come from taking what you learn in the group, and discussing and applying it in *your* marriage.

- ⊕ What was the shared vision that convinced you to marry each other? How well are you doing in pursuing that vision today? How has it evolved?

- ⊕ Can the two of you articulate today's shared vision for your marriage? What are you dreaming toward?

- ⊕ How well do you believe you do in pursuing intimacy vs. living in parallel play? Are there areas of marriage where parallel play works well? Are there areas you would like to move beyond parallel play and be more intimate?

- ⊟ Paul suggested the oneness of marriage is a mystery. What does it mean to pursue oneness in *your* marriage?

- ⊕ How well do each of you do in keeping your marriage about both the body and spirit of the act? In parenting? In finance? In your relationship with extended family? In spiritual matters?

If you are willing, also discuss a shared vision for your sexual intimacy:

- ⊕ What do you feel is the goal of most sexual encounters in your marriage? For you? For your spouse?

- ⊕ How well do you believe you (individually and as a couple) do in balancing both the body and spirit of the act through the entire course of your lovemaking?

- ⊕ Explore your couple vision for sexuality in your marriage. Spend time fleshing out what each of you would like to see over time. Include not just frequency, but style, practices, etc.

Note that when you come back together with your group, you can share about other areas of your vision during the Review time, but do not share details of your sexual vision.

Other Resources

See Chapter 10, *Secrets of Sex & Marriage,* for more about the theology of sex, including oneness and keeping sex incarnate.

Dr. Mike has a vision exercise for couples in the "Relationship Builders" section of IntimateMarriage.org.

An invitation to continue to Part Two

This study is intentionally divided into two parts of four sessions each.

Part One focused heavily on the setting required to develop an intimate marriage. The principles discussed in Part One all lay the foundation for Part Two. Each key discussed in Part 1 applies to all areas of marriage, including physical intimacy.

In **Part Two**, we begin to cover topics that are more specific to sexual intimacy in marriage while working to keep your couple physical intimacy sacred and to address both the spirit and body of intimacy..

We have worked hard to keep the group *discussions* safer, but the *teaching* is still on sex. We know not everyone will be comfortable with listening to teaching on sexual topics in a group setting, but we hope most of you will find it honoring, instructive, and helpful.

For the group time, we hope you have now seen that there *is* a way to keep group conversations comfortable, via the commitment to discuss private matters only at home and never during group time. In Part Two, we strengthen the boundaries to keep the conversation safe. For example, we will openly acknowledge sexual topics while "talking around them" during group time. Feel free to propose others to your group. If a discussion feels uncomfortable, flag the leader so the group can move on to the next video.

So we invite you to continue on.

If your group decides not to continue to Part Two, we invite you to consider working through this second part as a couple instead. (If necessary, see page 2 for how to access the videos on your own.) Adapt the questions as needed to spark conversations with each other. Remember Key #3 and stay curious, accepting, and gracious.

PART TWO

Keys to Sexual Intimacy

Welcome to Part Two of Unlocking an Intimate Marriage. Thank you for continuing to invest in your marriage in this way!

In these four sessions, we move more specifically into learning about keys to physical intimacy in marriage. To keep group discussions comfortable and helpful, you will see that discussion questions often use parallel topics – such as the desire for food, rather than the desire for sex – as a helpful but "safer" way to understand and discuss certain concepts. Honor one other by keeping the discussion within the boundaries set.

When we guide you into more sexual (but still not personal) subjects in the group discussion time, remember to keep couple sexual intimacy sacred. Be great group members and help gently structure each other if someone starts down a path that seems dishonoring or in a direction that will become unsafe. We highly recommend not even jokingly making sexual innuendos, as those might be received differently than you intend. That said, it is not uncommon to stumble into unintentional and sometimes hilarious double entendres. As long as everyone is respectful, we hope you will have grace with one another and laugh it off.

Enjoy this second part of the journey!

Energize the Process of Desire

Key #5

In this session we will focus on a factor that energizes the pursuit of physical intimacy: understanding the different **types** of desire. A shared vision can be energizing but is typically not enough in itself. We also want to understand the different types of desire, what they feel like, and how they do or don't apply to us and our spouse.

As you go through this session, remember: This study will be very helpful if you learn some practical, transformational knowledge and engage in community while doing so. It will be a true success if you and your spouse are also able to bring the conversation home and discuss how it applies to the two of **you.**

Review:

Last session we focused on the importance of vision and purpose. You were invited to assess how well you worked together vs. side by side. We also talked about pursuing a shared vision, creating oneness, and keeping our sex life incarnate (incorporating both body **_and_** spirit). Without sharing **what** you discussed in the area of sexual intimacy (keep it sacred), share if you set aside the time to talk with each other. Were you largely on the same page, or quite different?

notes

Naming Different Types of Desire

The recognition that there are different types of desire has been discussed by sex therapists for half a century. In discussing it, writers often use different terms.

When talking about what we call "initiating desire," some use the term "spontaneous desire" as it can seem to just appear without provocation. We don't use that term, because desire doesn't actually appear from nothing. Desire is a response to a cue – something internal (e.g., testosterone level) or external (e.g., something we experience as seductive). Even if it seems spontaneous, desire is never "out of the blue." It is always a response to something.

Others call this type of desire "assertive desire" as it is more forward moving. We used this language early on, as did some of the first sex therapists identifying these concepts. We no longer use that term, in part because the word "assertive" implies something about the emotional tone and power balance of sexual desire that we do not intend to convey.

For what we call "receptive desire," some use the term "responsive desire." While this term has been used in the past, we also do not use it today simply because, as mentioned, we now know that all types of desire are responding to something internal or external.

That being said, none of these terms are incorrect or harmful. Typically, something written using any of these terms can be helpful in exploring the various flavors of desire.

Discussion:

While discussing types of desire, we recommend you not reveal to the group the type of sexual desire you believe you or your spouse has. Discuss that only when you and your spouse are alone together.

- ❸ What are some examples of how popular culture represents desire in general (for example, for food, or to purchase a wanted Christmas present)? What is the message about how desire (non-sexual) "works"?

- ❸ How does our culture represent sexual desire, specifically? What is the message about how sexual desire "works"? What do you think is healthy/unhealthy about those messages?

- ⊕ By contrast, what type of desire does God have for us? How does this affect the way you see desire in marriage?

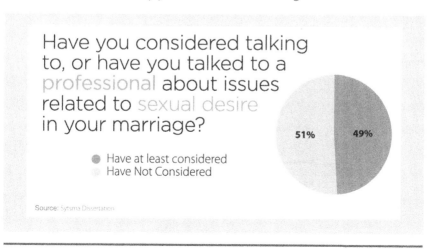

Have you considered talking to, or have you talked to a professional about issues related to sexual desire in your marriage?

51%   49%

● Have at least considered
  Have Not Considered

Source: Sytsma Dissertation

notes

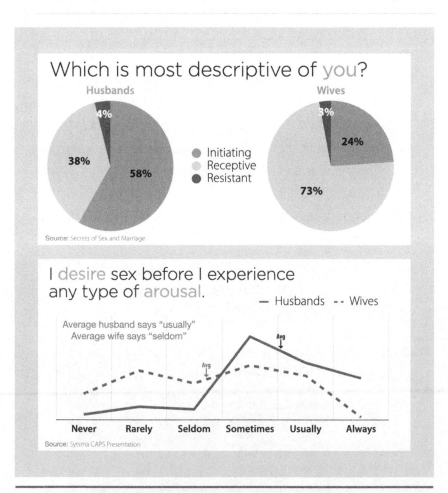

Which is most descriptive of you?

Husbands   Wives

- Initiating
- Receptive
- Resistant

Husbands: 4%, 38%, 58%

Wives: 3%, 24%, 73%

Source: Secrets of Sex and Marriage

I desire sex before I experience any type of arousal.

— Husbands   -- Wives

Average husband says "usually"
Average wife says "seldom"

Never   Rarely   Seldom   Sometimes   Usually   Always

Source: Sytsma CAPS Presentation

Discussion:

Consider how initiating desire works, via these questions. Remember to keep the group safe by not discussing sexual topics until alone with your spouse.

- ✪ Share with the group what foods you tend to have initiating desire for. What is that experience like for you? In other words, how does that type of initiating desire for a certain food feel and play out for you?
- ❶ If that initiating desire is ever unhealthy, how do you keep it in check?
- ✪ Are there other things in life (beyond sexual things) that you tend to have an initiating desire for? Maybe certain types of purchases or experiences?

VIDEO 5.3 RECEPTIVE DESIRE

notes

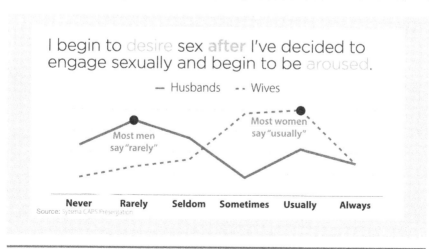

I begin to desire sex after I've decided to engage sexually and begin to be aroused.

— Husbands   - - Wives

Most men say "rarely"

Most women say "usually"

| Never | Rarely | Seldom | Sometimes | Usually | Always |

Source: Sytsma CAPS Presentation

Desire in marriage

		WIVES		
		Initiating 23.6%	Receptive 73.1%	Resistant 3.3%
HUSBANDS	Initiating 58.5%	10.0%	46.1%	2.4%
	Receptive 37.6%	12.4%	24.5%	0.7%
	Resistant 3.9%	12.4%	24.5%	0.7%

Discussion:

Discuss receptive desire using the following questions. Remember to keep the group safe by not discussing sexual topics until alone with your spouse.

- Share with the group what foods you tend to have receptive desire for. What is that experience like for you? What does it take for the desire for that food to kick in?

- Does the setting make a difference in your desire for food/drink? Are you more likely to desire something specific when in a particular setting?

- Are there other things in life (beyond sexual things) that you tend to have a receptive desire for? Maybe certain types of purchases or experiences?

- Do you have a bias toward one type of desire or another? Do you believe initiating desire for something might be a "more legitimate" desire?

notes

VIDEO 4 BRINGING IT HOME

notes

BRINGING IT HOME

As you know, connecting on these topics at home is a crucial part of this study. Please set aside an uninterrupted time to do so (no devices or kids) before the next group session. Growth and change will come from taking what you learn in the group, and discussing and applying it in *your* marriage.

- Pay attention to your own desires this week. Watch for your experience of desire for different foods, for exercise, private worship, work, time with family, and so on. Do you see times of initiating desire? Times of receptive desire?

- Have a heart-to-heart talk with your spouse about the type of desire each of you experience in various areas of life.

- Then, talk with each other about the type of sexual desire *you* most typically experience. What does that feel like for each of you? Does this help explain certain things you hadn't understood about one another – or about yourself? Stay curious about each other, remembering both types of desire are healthy and normal.

- Read Chapter 4 of *Secrets of Sex & Marriage.* Now that you know your desire-type pattern, what actions and solutions might work best for the two of you, to improve your ability to connect?

notes

_____

_____

_____

_____

_____

_____

_____

_____

_____

_____

_____

_____

_____

_____

Other Resources

SecretsofSexandMarriage.com is our central site for specialized resources on sexual intimacy. This includes articles and referral resources in specific areas of need (resistant desire, sexual pain, sexual compulsions like pornography, and other topics). It also includes links to streaming courses.

Chapter 4, *Secrets of Sex & Marriage.*

Find Dr. Sytsma's streaming course on sexual desire in marriage at SexualDesireinMarriage.com. Use code UNLOCKINGSTUDY for discount.

Be Purposeful About Desire

Key #6

As you now know, multiple factors running under the surface will impact when and how we feel desire. Just as there are different *types* of desire (Session 5), there are also different *levels* of desire that move us forward. But intentionality can keep us moving when desire goes weak or when we encounter obstacles. As a result, becoming purposeful and intentional about desire is vitally important to connecting as a couple and building sexual intimacy.

As you go through this session, remember: This study will be very helpful if you learn some practical, transformational knowledge and engage in community while doing so. It will be a true success if you and your spouse are also able to bring the conversation home and discuss how it applies to the two of *you.*

Review:

Last session we focused on initiating and receptive sexual desire. We talked about how the initiating type of sexual desire tends to lead arousal, and the receptive type of sexual desire tends to follow arousal. Outside of sex (honor the group by not referencing sexual examples), did you notice any examples of initiating and receptive desire in your life this week? (e.g., food, purchases, experiences.) Take a minute to share some examples with your group.

How often are couples having sex?

People often ask, "How often should we have sex?" But there is no one "right" frequency of connection. The question is: What is right for you as a couple? The answer will depend on many factors (age, ages of children, physical health, trauma, health of the relationship, medications you take, your job schedules, and so on).

As you can see below, there is a wide range of sexual frequency among married couples (which includes all sexual connection, not just intercourse). A few notes to consider, depending on where you and your spouse fall:

Once a week or more. Sex therapists tend to see positive outcomes in the marriage when a couple generally connects once a week or more. We saw this in the data as well. Of course, this frequency is not always feasible – different seasons of life and situations in the relationship may call for another pattern. And this frequency obviously has to be in a healthy context. But many marriages see positive outcomes from making this frequency a priority.

Between once a month and once a week. Many couples have found both spouses are happy with this pattern, including as they get older. Other couples would like more connection but find obstacles getting in the way. For example, perhaps one spouse is longing to connect more often, but the other spouse travels away from home for work, is taking a medicine that interferes, or is exhausted from a busy work schedule. In those cases, therapists recommend that both spouses apply both intentionality (we talk about this in Session 8), and grace (being realistic and accepting the impact of the demands of the season).

Less than once a month, or never. In our survey, there was a concerningly high level of "sexless" marriages (defined as less than once a month or never). While this is sometimes just temporary (for example, while recovering from childbirth or surgery), most therapists recommend a couple address it if the disconnect has gone on for more than a few months. Even when physical issues are involved (for example, dryness, arousal problems, pain), most couples can find ways to be sexual together for their entire lives if they are creative and make it a priority. Perhaps because sex often smooths out relationship friction, its absence can lead to other problems in the marriage. See SecretsofSexandMarriage.com for referral resources to help you reconnect in this important area.

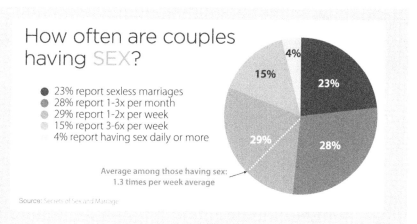

How often are couples having SEX?

- 23% report sexless marriages
- 28% report 1-3x per month
- 29% report 1-2x per week
- 15% report 3-6x per week
- 4% report having sex daily or more

Average among those having sex:
1.3 times per week average

Source: Secrets of Sex and Marriage

VIDEO 6.1 DESIRE LEVELS

notes

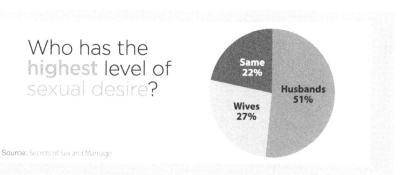

Who has the highest level of sexual desire?

Same 22%
Husbands 51%
Wives 27%

Source: Secrets of Sex and Marriage

Discussion:

Keep the group safe. Do not reveal to the group your desire level, your spouse's desire level, or who tends to be higher or lower in your marriage.

- ❶ Other than sex, consider the enjoyable things we might desire to do together. (Wander the aisles of the mall or DIY store, go camping, grill out on the patio, take in the latest movie on opening weekend …) How do you usually navigate it when one person has a greater desire to do that activity than the other? Is there an even better way to handle it?

- ❷ Do you ever think your spouse is a bit "off" for enjoying something with lower (or greater) intensity than you do? (e.g., foods, sports, hobbies, art, etc.) Are some things just a personal preference, and that's okay? Or do you think we should always be able to change our desire levels?

- ❸ What do you think our popular culture says our level of sexual desire should be? Do you think culture gives a different message for men and women?

- ❸ What do you think the church culture teaches our level of sexual desire should be? Does it suggest a different level for men and women?

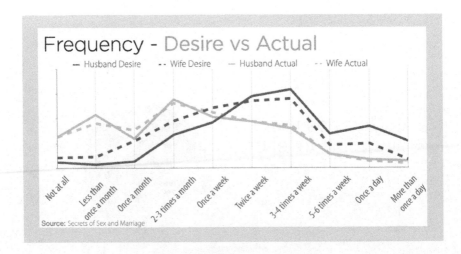

Frequency - Desire vs Actual

— Husband Desire   - - Wife Desire   — Husband Actual   - - Wife Actual

Not at all / Less than once a month / Once a month / 2-3 times a month / Once a week / Twice a week / 3-4 times a week / 5-6 times a week / Once a day / More than once a day

Source: Secrets of Sex and Marriage

Sexual Pain as a Hindrance

An additional hindrance to sexual desire is the presence of pain. Sexual pain, especially in women, has been identified as an epidemic due to the high frequency and poor treatment rates. In our survey, 31% of women and 12% of men reported genital pain at least every third time they had sex. For women, this pain interferes with pleasure a high percentage of the time.

If you or your spouse experience pain during sex, please see our articles at SecretsofSexandMarriage.com for guidance and additional information.

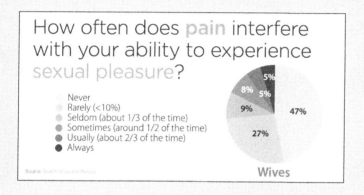

 VIDEO 6.2 INTENTIONAL DESIRE

notes

Where do you fit

		TYPE OF DESIRE		
		Initiating	Receptive	Resistant
DESIRE LEVEL (compared to your spouse)	I have higher desire			
	We are the same			
	I have lower desire			

Discussion:

- ☉ Using a non-sexual example, what is your internal experience of intentional desire, and why do you make the choice? For example, what foods do you have an intentional desire for? What activities do you tend to do out of intentional desire? (For example, exercise, keeping a budget …)
- ☉ Can you see intentional desire that is stirred up by choice as a legitimate type of desire?
- ☉ What type of desire do you tend to have for God? Initiating? Receptive? Resistant? Intentional? All of the above?

 VIDEO 6.3 DESIRE HINDRANCES AND HELPS

notes

Discussion:

Keep the group safe. Do not reveal to the group your desire level or your spouse's desire level or who tends to be higher or lower in your marriage.

- ⊙ What creates a hindrance to certain foods or (non-sexual) experiences for you? For example, people tend to be resistant toward certain foods because of bad past experiences, personal preference ("I just don't like it"), or fear of what it could do to them (e.g., allergens). Talk about a food (or experience) you tend to have a resistant desire toward. How do you explain why you are resistant to it?

- ❗ When a fear (a "push away" from something –internal or external) is instinctive or even irrational, what can you do to move beyond it?

- ⊙ How do you go about increasing your desire for something? (As always, non-sexual examples only.)

- ⊕ How well do you do in staying healthy overall? (Sleep, exercise, eating well, managing stress …) Since physical health matters for many things in life, what realistic steps might you take to improve it?

 VIDEO 6.4 BRINGING IT HOME

notes

BRINGING IT HOME

As you know, connecting on these topics at home is a crucial part of this study. Please set aside an uninterrupted time to do so (no devices or kids) before the next group session. Growth and change will come from taking what you learn in the group, and discussing and applying it in *your* marriage.

Remember to be curious, accepting, and to extend grace. Stay focused on the positive vision, rather than the areas you might wish were different.

- ❗ Where do you each fall on the grid of Type of Desire and Desire Level (page 58)? Does anything about that surprise you, or have implications for how you two connect sexually?

- ↻ How would you describe your level of sexual desire just before your wedding? What about a year after your wedding? How would you describe it today? Any noteworthy highs and lows over the course of your marriage? What do you believe has influenced your level of desire over the course of your marriage?

- ↻ Pick one area from your shared vision (Session 4) that you want to intentionally work on this week.

- ↻ What is one thing you personally could do that might help you move one baby step closer to the vision the two of you have for your marriage?

- ↻ What stands in the way of you being intentional in pursuing the vision? What can you do that might remove that obstacle? Finally, is there anything you've been believing about your spouse and how they feel sexually that you might need to reassess?

Other Resources

Secrets of Sex and Marriage by Shaunti Feldhahn and Michael Sytsma – Chapters 4 and 5.

Find Dr. Mike's streaming course on sexual desire in marriage at SexualDesireinMarriage.com. Use code UNLOCKINGSTUDY for discount.

Additional resources available at SecretsofSexandMarriage.com

Learn How to Initiate and Enjoy

Key  #7

Understanding and creating a mutually understood process of initiation is another very overlooked factor in helping couples connect well and avoid disappointment or pressure. So is ensuring we are attending to pleasure. So in this session we will focus on initiating a sexual encounter with our spouse,[2] knowing what we are initiating, and then making sure that we are mindful for the rest of the process.

As you go through this session, remember: This study will be very helpful if you learn some practical, transformational knowledge and engage in community while doing so. It will be a true success if you and your spouse are also able to bring the conversation home and discuss how it applies to the two of *you.*

Review:

In the last few sessions we focused on desire. We talked about initiating desire, receptive desire, and briefly about resistant desire. We also discussed the importance of intentionality, or intentional desire.

One of the things everyone has trouble with occasionally is being intentional about doing things that are good for them and/or others – such as eating healthy or taking the time to play with the kids when there are million other things to do. During your Bringing it Home time you discussed what obstacles can get in the way of intentionality. Outside of sex (honor the group by not referencing sexual examples), share with your group what some of those obstacles are, and how we overcome them.*

---

[2] In Dr. Sytsma's Intimacy Model, this is called "spark" as we are igniting the fire we have spent so long laying the foundation for. See more at IntimacyModel.com.

VIDEO 7.1 HAVE A PROCESS FOR INITIATING SEX

notes

Discussion:

As always, keep the group safe. Do not discuss ways you or our spouse initiate sex.

- ⊕ Completely aside from sex, all of us have other things we would like in our marriage. How do you ask your spouse for those things? For example, how do you let them know what you would like for dinner, or that you'd prefer they drove carpool this week, or that you need to cancel the game night with friends because you're just not feeling up to it?

- ❶ Consider: What is the tone or direction of your way of letting them know what you would like? Is it invitational? Somewhat demanding? Too passive? Are you clear?

- ⊕ How well does your way work? Do you truly give your spouse permission to say "no" or suggest something else?

notes

Discussion:

- What are some examples of non-sexual situations where we want to have boundaries agreed upon before we are willing to step into them? (For example, a risky business deal, an athletic contest, etc.) What do these agreed-upon boundaries allow us to do?

- Are you more adventurous or cautious in life? Are you more spontaneous or do you want to know the rules and boundaries first? How does this personality trait play out in your marriage? How does it play out in how you initiate what you would like in life?

- Think of some (non-sexual) examples of where you might have to turn down a sensitive request from someone you have an ongoing relationship with. How do you want that person to handle the news? How would you view them going forward if they handled it the way you preferred? How would you view them going forward if they handled it in a way you don't like?

VIDEO 7.3 BE PRESENT WITH THE SENSATIONS

notes

Discussion:

As always, keep the group safe. Do not discuss sensuality in sex.

- Thinking about "sensual" as "experiencing the senses," in what non-sexual arenas do you tend to embrace and savor a sensual experience and associate it with positive emotions? (Tasting a particular food, hearing music, the feel of physical exertion, smelling Christmas cookies …)
- In what arenas do you tend to rush through the experience of the senses instead of savoring it? Why is that? Might some experiences *become* a positive engagement of the senses, if you were to handle them in a different way? What actions might lead to that?

VIDEO 7.4 BRINGING IT HOME

notes

BRINGING IT HOME

As you know, connecting on these topics at home is a crucial part of this study. Please set aside an uninterrupted time to do so (no devices or kids) before the next group session. Growth and change will come from taking what you learn in the group, and discussing and applying it in *your* marriage.

Remember to be curious, accepting, and to extend grace as you talk through ways you might be very different but both want to connect well.

> **Important note:** This "Bringing It Home" section is more intermediate-level work. Only try the suggestions for the items **both** of you are comfortable with.

Discuss:

❶ What signals of initiation or openness (and/or scheduling) will work for us, so we know what is being asked for and how to respond?

❷ How do each of us handle giving and receiving a "no"? Is there a way we can increase our skill in saying or receiving, "the timing isn't right?" rather than a more painful message?

❸ In various situations and with various signals, **who** should be the person initiating – keeping in mind who has what type of desire?

Personal Reflection:

- If you and your spouse have different types of desire, do you feel like it "shouldn't" be that way? How can you work through that in your own mind and heart, and in your relationship with God, rather than placing that expectation on your spouse?
- What does cuddling, making out, and having sex mean to you? Where are the lines?

Practice:

- During non-sexual times, practice being mindful of and savoring various inputs from the senses. Share with each other what you are learning and realizing.
- During your next time of sexual intimacy, practice slowing down a bit and drinking in the sensations rather than rushing through the "making out" stage and straight to the sex stage. Then discuss it afterward.
- Practice honoring a time where one person asks, "let's just cuddle tonight." Now that you know where the line is, do not go past that line. Discuss it afterward. How did that go? Did it make you feel safe? Free to set aside anxiety? Frustrated? What lessons did you learn?

Other Resources

Chapter 8, Secrets of Sex & Marriage.

See IntimacyModel.com for a video introducing Dr. Sytsma's Intimacy Model, which describes the stages and cycle of sexual intimacy. Use the code "UNLOCKINGSTUDY" for a discount off the streaming cost. OR read Chapter 13 – Marital Sexuality in the book *Sanctified Sexuality: Valuing Sex in an Oversexed World* edited by Sandra Glahn and Gary Barnes (2020, Kregel Academic).

You can also hear Dr. Mike in *The Art of Initiation*, a streaming talk available at IntimateMarriage.org/initiation.

Practice the Art of Invitation

Key #8

In our final session, we will affirm the importance of being invitational (rather than directive or pushy) as we apply everything we have learned. We will never do it perfectly, but we can continue to have grace with one another. We can continue to focus on those things that are lovely and worthy of praise in one another.

We encourage you to use the wrap-up of this study as the beginning of an ongoing commitment to develop intimacy in your marriage. Consider reading through **Secrets of Sex & Marriage** together out loud, pausing often to discuss, to continue the conversation. Or, consider one of the online courses available through SecretsofSexandMarriage.com.

As you go through this final session, remember: This study will be very helpful if you learn some practical, transformational knowledge and engage in community while doing so. It will be a true success if you and your spouse are also able to bring the conversation home and discuss how it applies to the two of **you.**

Review:

In the last session we focused on creating a good process for initiation and being mindful of the senses. Without sharing anything sexual, share with the group what you learned from the practice of mindfulness. Did you feel the intentional focus awakened your senses at all? Had no impact? Was it difficult to be mindful? Is that an exercise you want to continue?

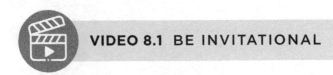

VIDEO 8.1 BE INVITATIONAL

notes

> *"Look! I stand at the door and knock.*
> *If you hear my voice and open the door, I will come in,*
> *and we will share a meal together as friends."*
>
> *- Revelation 3:20*

Discussion:

Avoid sexual examples in group and speak only for yourself, not for your spouse.

- In what areas do you struggle with being invitational instead of demanding or commanding? (Work? With your children? With your spouse?) In what areas are you pretty good at being invitational?

- What helps you to be invitational? How can you apply that to the areas that need more invitation and less pushiness?

- Can you remember someone in your life who was more demanding of you? What did that feel like? Can you remember someone in your life who was more invitational of you? What was that experience like? What lesson can you take from that for marriage?

- What has your experience of God been? Have you been taught or have the feeling that God is demanding or invitational? Can you share some examples?

VIDEO 8.2 LIVE SEDUCTIVELY

notes

Discussion:

- What was your initial reaction to the word "seduction"? What is it now that you've heard this way of thinking about it?
- Outside of sexual things, what woos you or draws you in life? What do you find seductive? (e.g., sports cars, beautiful shoes, kittens, etc.) Do you feel you *allow* those things to be seductive to you?
- Beyond marriage and sex, are there areas of your life (work, kids, athletics, activities …) where you might benefit from being "seduced" or drawn in by something, but you do not allow yourself to be drawn in? Why is that? How might you overcome that?
- If someone was *living* seductively around their spouse, what might that look like? Identify at least ten *non-sexual* elements (words, actions, attitudes …) that might characterize someone who was living seductively.

VIDEO 8.3 BASK IN YOUR CONNECTION

notes

Discussion:

As always, keep the discussion focused on the group learning. Protect the sacredness of your marriage.

- What was the most significant learning for you in our time together as a group?
- What was your experience of exploring this material in community?
- Have you made any commitments to change that you can share with the group?

VIDEO 8.4 BRINGING IT HOME

notes

But don't just listen to God's word. You must do what it says. Otherwise, you are only fooling yourselves.

For if you listen to the word and don't obey, it is like glancing at your face in a mirror. You see yourself, walk away, and forget what you look like.

But if you look carefully into the perfect law that sets you free, and if you do what it says and don't forget what you heard, then God will bless you for doing it.

- James 1:22-25

Intimacy Model by Dr. Michael Sytsma

See IntimacyModel.com for a video introduction to Dr. Sytsma's Intimacy Model, which describes the stages and cycle of sexual intimacy. (Use the code "UNLOCKINGSTUDY" for a 50% discount on the streaming cost.)

Or read Chapter 13, "Marital Sexuality" in the book *Sanctified Sexuality: Valuing Sex in an Oversexed World* edited by Sandra Glahn and Gary Barnes (2020, Kregel Academic).

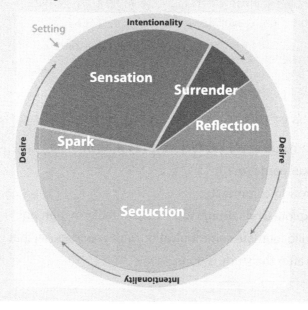

 **BRINGING IT HOME**

Even after the study draws to a close, please continue to set aside time to discuss the application of *all* that you have learned. Consider continuing to write in the workbook, or keeping a journal to capture what you are learning.

A Note from Dr. Michael Sytsma

The most important thing in moving forward is being intentional. Deciding to consistently implement some kind of change is everything.

If you have already built the practice of a weekly "working date," I recommend you continue that habit on an ongoing basis. (At a minimum, please do it for at least the next four weeks to continue your discussion of these topics.)

If you have not, please consider beginning to regularly have "Working Dates" so to give yourself the best opportunity to further solidify the positive gains from this study and continue to grow. As noted at the beginning, when these "business meetings for your marriage" are done consistently, they can often facilitate rapid transformation. A simple instruction sheet is available at:

IntimateMarriage.org/workingdate.

Our goals of this study – including going forward – are:

- To learn and apply key factors to creating intimacy in your marriage;
- To grow in community;
- To explore God's design for sexual intimacy in marriage;
- To build intimate communication with your spouse, that will last long after the study is done.

Discussion:

Here are questions to ponder and discuss moving forward.

Look at the Goals of the study on page 72. Our overall goal in this study has been to unlock intimacy – of all types – in your marriage. So consider your intimacy in communication, sexual relationship, spiritual life, emotional closeness, and so on.

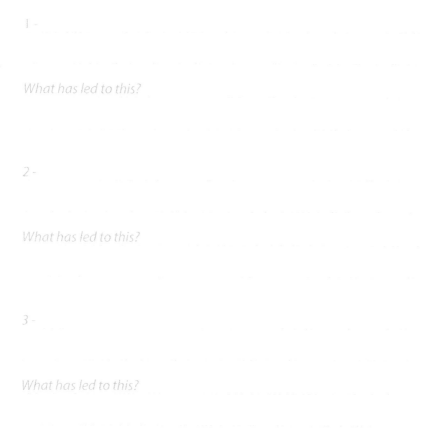

- In what areas have we improved the most during this study? (Identify together and write a list of the top three areas that you can celebrate.)
- By each item, identify what specifically you believe has led to that area of improvement.

1 -

What has led to this?

2 -

What has led to this?

3 -

What has led to this?

What do we want to work on?

- In what areas do you still need to grow? Identify together and write a list of the top three areas that you most want and need to work on.
- By each item, identify what specific action steps you will take next to continue working on those things. (This should be something you can look back on and say whether you've completed it or not. "Try harder" is not an action step. Make it measurable.)

1 -

Action step...

2 -

Action step...

3 -

Action step...

- If you have not already done so via your "working date" (see *A note from Dr. Michael Sytsma* on pagepage 72) schedule at least four times on your calendar to talk during the next weeks and months, when you will discuss and evaluate those items and action steps, or add new ones.
- As a next step, if you have not yet done so, read through *Secrets of Sex & Marriage* out loud to one another, sharing with each other your thoughts and how it applies to each of you, as you go.

Other Resources

For your next steps on the journey, see our streaming courses at SecretsofSexandMarriage.com.

If you haven't already, read *Secrets of Sex & Marriage* out loud to one another, and discuss.

Consider some of the other resources available on our websites:

ThriveinLoveandMoney.com - An excellent study for couples want to work on financial intimacy.

IntimateMarriage.org - Especially the Relationship Builders section and the Listen/Learn section.

Thank you for joining us -- and for investing in your marriage!

We would love your feedback.

Jump over to our anonymous form and let us know about your experience with this material. We greatly value it.

https://UnlockinganIntimateMarriage.com/feedback

notes

Deeper Into the Word

The *Unlocking an Intimate Marriage* small-group study is particularly designed for people of faith, and people exploring faith. Principles, passages and discussions from the Bible are woven throughout all eight sessions. However, some small groups will want to allow for extra time and go deeper into discussing scripture and the application of specific biblical principles. Others may wish to use these questions to go deeper into their discussions as a couple, or their personal devotions time. This section is designed for those groups and individuals.

Our goal with this additional study is to help us keep an eternal perspective always before our mind, so we consider how to glorify and follow God every day as we work on our marriage.

If you choose to discuss these questions in your group, we recommend you work them into the regular flow of the session, rather than at the beginning or the end. After going through the relevant video and key discussion questions (which are important to unpack a specific application), then come to the related "Deeper Into the Word" section and dive into the deeper scriptural discussion. When ready, resume the regular flow of the session with the next video.

As always, keep group discussion safe, and honoring of your spouse.

Session One

In Session One, we unpack God's recipe for restoring our first love in Him: Remember. Repent. Do. Let's go deeper into how that direction applies to our relationship with God and our relationship with our spouse.

Scripture:

> "I know that you have persevered and endured hardships for the sake of my name, and you have not grown weary. But I have this against you: You have abandoned the love you had at first. Remember then how far you have fallen; repent, and do the works you did at first. Otherwise, I will come to you and remove your lampstand from its place, unless you repent."
> -Revelation 2:3-5 (CSB)

> "The passion of love bursting into flame is more powerful than death, stronger than the grave. Love cannot be drowned by oceans or floods. It cannot be bought – any offer would be scorned no matter how great."
> - Song of Solomon 8:6b-7 (CEV)

Discussion:

These questions are designed to be used after watching Video 2 and discussing the questions on page 14.

- How does God praise the believers in Revelation 2:3? Why does that not "cancel out" what He criticizes them for?
- Revelation 2:3-5 is talking about a body of believers in a city. But how might it also apply to a marriage? Specifically, what are the ways the love in a marriage might have "fallen"?
- "Remember, Repent and Do" is the solution given for the church. Building on the Video 2 discussion, specifically how might that also help a married couple?
- In a marriage, what leads to "the passion of love bursting into flame"?

Session Two

In Session Two, we discuss that an essential part of marriage is communication, and an essential part of communication is listening. As believers, we know that communication with and listening to God is vital as well. Let's explore what the Bible says about both of those things.

Scripture:

> *"The gatekeeper opens the gate for him, and the sheep recognize his voice and come to him. He calls his own sheep by name and leads them out. After he has gathered his own flock, he walks ahead of them, and they follow him because they know his voice. They won't follow a stranger; they will run from him because they don't know his voice ... My sheep listen to my voice; I know them, and they follow me."*
>
> *- John 10:3-5, 27*

> *"'For I know the plans I have for you,' says the LORD. 'They are plans for good and not for disaster, to give you a future and a hope. In those days when you pray, I will listen. If you look for me wholeheartedly, you will find me.'"*
>
> *- Jeremiah 29:11-13*

Discussion:

These questions are designed to be used after watching Video 2 and discussing the questions on page 21.

- In John 10, what key factor allows the sheep to "recognize" the voice of the Shepherd rather than the voice of the stranger?
- How do we listen to God's voice, so we can follow Him?
- What might we learn from that about listening to our spouse?
- According to Jeremiah 29:11-13, how does God listen to us? What does verse 11 imply about his intentions toward us?
- How might that same factor apply to our willingness to listen to our spouse?

Session Three

In Session Three, we explore the vital attitudes of curiosity, acceptance, and grace. In what ways might God's direction in Philippians 4 help us apply these attitudes in our relationship with God and with others in our life?

Scripture:

> *"Always be full of joy in the Lord. I say it again – rejoice! Let everyone see that you are considerate in all you do. ... Don't worry about anything; instead, pray about everything. Tell God what you need, and thank him for all he has done. Then you will experience God's peace, which exceeds anything we can understand. His peace will guard your hearts and minds as you live in Christ Jesus. And now, dear brothers and sisters, one final thing. Fix your thoughts on what is true, and honorable, and right, and pure, and lovely, and admirable. Think about things that are excellent and worthy of praise."*
>
> *- Philippians 4:4-8*

Discussion:

These questions are designed to be used after watching Video 3.4 - Bringing It Home. See pagepage 30.

- Read Philippians 4:2-9. Paul's direction to the church in Philippians 4:8 comes on the heels of him pleading with two women in the church to settle their disagreement and be restored to one another. How might we apply this same admonition to the broken parts of a marriage relationship? What might that action do in our hearts in the process?
- Other than marriage, give an example of an area in which it is easy to be frustrated and critical. What specifically might change in that area, if you choose the actions outlined in verse 4 of the Philippians passage? Verse 6?

Session Four

Session Four focuses on God's design for "one-ness" in marriage. What does the Bible say about one-ness, and how it works in marriage and in our relationship with God?

Scripture:

> Then the LORD God said, "It is not good for the man to be alone. I will make a helper who is just right for him." … So the LORD God caused the man to fall into a deep sleep. While the man slept, the LORD God took out one of the man's ribs and closed up the opening. Then the LORD God made a woman from the rib, and he brought her to the man.
>
> "At last!" the man exclaimed.
> "This one is bone from my bone,
> and flesh from my flesh!
> She will be called 'woman,'
> because she was taken from 'man.'"
>
> This explains why a man leaves his father and mother and is joined to his wife, and the two are united into one.
> *-Genesis 2:18, 21-24*
>
> "And I give myself as a holy sacrifice for them so they can be made holy by your truth. I pray that [my disciples down through history] will all be one, just as you and I are one —as you are in me, Father, and I am in you.
> And may they be in us so that the world will believe you sent me.
> I have given them the glory you gave me,
> so they may be one as we are one.
> I am in them and you are in me.
> May they experience such perfect unity
> that the world will know that you sent me
> and that you love them as much as you love me."
> *- John 17:20-23*
>
> "As the Scriptures say, 'A man leaves his father and mother and is joined to his wife, and the two are united into one.' This is a great mystery, but it is an illustration of the way Christ and the church are one."
>
> *- Ephesians 5:31-32*

Discussion:

These questions are designed to be used after watching Video 4.2 and discussing the questions on page 35.

- Read Genesis 2:18, 21-24. There are countless ways in which God could have made a woman. Do you think it is significant that He chose to form her the way He did? What might be the reason that she was formed from the rib of Adam?

- In John 17:19-23 we see that the ideal unity with God and Christ in some mysterious way shows everyone that God sent Jesus into the world to save them. Do you think our unity with our spouse is intended to similarly reflect Christ to an unbelieving world? Have you ever thought that your efforts to become one with your spouse could draw people to Christ? What might that mean for your efforts toward oneness in marriage?

- Read Ephesians 5:31-32. God has called us to be more than friends or companions, He has called us to one-ness. Why do you think He created marriage in that way? What do you think "one-ness" actually means, on a day to day basis? (Privately, consider: how are you, personally, doing at living in that way every day?)

Session Five

Session Five explores the different types of desire, and how it applies to marriage. Does it also apply in our relationship with God?

Scripture:

> *"This is good and pleases God our Savior, who wants everyone to be saved and to understand the truth."*
>
> *- 1 Timothy 2:3-4*

> *"We love because he first loved us."*
>
> *-1 John 4:19 (NIV)*

Discussion:

These questions are designed to be used after watching Video 5.1 and discussing the questions on page 47.

- A quick look through a topical Bible will show a host of Bible verses speaking of God's desire for us, including Paul's words to Timothy. Does this seem to reflect a more initiating or receptive desire?
- Can we trigger a desire in God's heart (receptive desire), or is He always pursuing us?
- Read 1 John 4:19. Does this seem like receptive desire to you?
- If God regularly calls us to respond to His love and follow Him, how does this inform your view of receptive desire?

Session Six

In Session Six we further investigate how desire works, and the importance and power of being intentional. Let's continue that investigation here with how those factors impact all areas of our life as followers of Jesus.

Scripture:

> *"Blessed are those who hunger and thirst for righteousness, for they will be filled."*
> *- Matthew 5:6 (NIV)*

> *"Then, going over to the people who sold doves, he told them, 'Get these things out of here. Stop turning my Father's house into a marketplace!'*
> *Then his disciples remembered this prophecy from the Scriptures: 'Passion for God's house will consume me.'"*
> *– John 2:16-17*

> *"… Instead, train yourself to be godly. 'Physical training is good, but training for godliness is much better, promising benefits in this life and in the life to come.'"*
> *-1 Timothy 4:7b-8*

Discussion:

These questions are designed to be used after watching Video 6.2 and discussing the questions on page 58.

- Read Matthew 5:6 and John 2:16-17. The ideal might be to always have an initiating desire for righteousness as Jesus describes. In watching Him drive out the money-changers, Christ's followers were reminded of Psalm 69:9, "Passion for your house has consumed me" Is that basically the same thing as a strong sense of desire? What are some areas of your walk with the Lord in which you have strong initiating desire for righteousness?
- Read Timothy 4:7-8. In some areas we may practice intentional desire because the pursuit of Godliness is who we want to be, even if we don't feel it in the moment. When we practice intentional desire and engage in the spiritual disciplines, how

does that impact our feeling of desire for God? How does that impact our feeling about the disciplines? What are some areas of spiritual discipline where you can be more intentional?

- As with sex, we must watch for resistant desire in our relationship with God. But in that particular love relationship, resistant desire is not always bad. For a season, while we work through hurt or fear, how might an initial sense of resistant desire end up being meaningful?

- Scripture is filled with people who, in their hurt or anger, are resistant to God. Can you think of some examples? Can you think of an area in your relationship with God, your life or your marriage (other than sex) where you have resistant desire? How might that be used by God in the end? How can you pray through it to grow in that area?

Session Seven

In Session Seven, we explore reaching out to our spouse for sexual intimacy. Let's explore what the Bible says about *how* to approach one another with requests, including in challenging or vulnerable moments.

Scripture:

Is there any encouragement from belonging to Christ? Any comfort from his love? Any fellowship together in the Spirit? Are your hearts tender and compassionate? Then make me truly happy by agreeing wholeheartedly with each other, loving one another, and working together with one mind and purpose.

Don't be selfish; don't try to impress others. Be humble, thinking of others as better than yourselves. Don't look out only for your own interests, but take an interest in others, too.
- Philippians 2:1-4

Let us think of ways to motivate one another to acts of love and good works.
-Hebrews 10:24

Don't use foul or abusive language. Let everything you say be good and helpful, so that your words will be an encouragement to those who hear them.
-Ephesians 4:29

Instead, be kind to each other, tenderhearted, forgiving one another, just as God through Christ has forgiven you.
- Ephesians 4:32 (NIV)

Love is patient and kind. Love is not jealous or boastful or proud or rude. It does not demand its own way. It is not irritable, and it keeps no record of being wronged. It does not rejoice about injustice but rejoices whenever the truth wins out. Love never gives up, never loses faith, is always hopeful, and endures through every circumstance.
- I Corinthians 13:4-7

Discussion:

These questions are designed to be used after watching Video 7.1 and discussing the questions on page 62.

- Read Philippians 2:1-4. What does the first half of the sentence (belonging to Christ, having comfort from his love, and so on), have to do with the second half of the sentence ("agreeing wholeheartedly with each other," and so on)?

- Other than sex, identify some meaningful areas in marriage, in which our desires might be different than that of our spouse. If we are to be united to our spouse in oneness, what does this scripture mean for us when our desires are different?

- What might Philippians 2 mean for how we ask our spouse for things? Consider what it might mean for how we request simple things (where we want to go for dinner), big things (a request to clean out the basement this weekend), and vulnerable things (a request that your spouse continue to listen, even when they are upset). How can this description of relating change the way you approach your spouse?

- A request involves both an approach and a response of some kind. Read Hebrews 10:24 and Ephesians 4:29. How might a request for our spouse "motivate one another to acts of love and good works" instead of being unwholesome or unhelpful?

- How do we handle it when we or our spouse don't get our approach or response right? Read Ephesians 4:32 and I Corinthians 13:4-7 and list all the ways we can treat each other that will encourage ongoing change, rather than shutting one another down because of mistakes.

Session Eight

In Session Eight we wrap up our study with a discussion of how Jesus is invitational with us, and how we can be invitational with our spouse. Let's further explore what our response to God's invitation should be, and how to move forward well in our relationship with our spouse and our relationship with Him.

Scripture:

Abide in Me, and I in you.

- John 15:4

Jesus called out to them,
"Come, follow me, and I will show you how to fish for people!"

-Mark 1:17

Then Jesus said, "Come to me, all of you who are weary and carry heavy burdens, and I will give you rest.

-Matthew 11:28

Trust in the Lord with all your heart;
do not depend on your own understanding.

Seek his will in all you do,
and he will show you which path to take.

– Proverbs 3:5-6

Discuss:

These questions are designed to be used after watching Video 8.1 and discussing the questions on page 68.

- What is God's invitation to us in John 15:4? What does "abiding" with God mean to you? How does that look in your life, currently? (If you are not sure what that means, see the Personal Reflection section after the group discussion.)
- Read Mark 1:17. After God first invited His disciples to Himself, what was his next invitation? What does that mean, and do you think that invitation applies to all of us in some way? If so, how might our marriage be a part of that calling?

- List two or three examples of what it might mean to "follow" God? List two or three examples of what it might mean to serve your spouse.
- As we wrap up this study, we may have made a great deal of progress in some areas of building intimacy, and in others we may have been working for years and still feel like we are not getting anywhere. Without sharing any specific details of continued frustrations, what do Matthew 11:28 and Proverbs 3:5-6 imply about how we should view those areas? On a practical, day-to-day basis, what would it look like to truly rest and trust in the Lord and allow Him to bring transformation?

Personal Reflection:

In addition to talking through the above questions as a couple and a group, the following are important for you to reflect on individually.

- Do you believe the selflessness, growth, grace, acceptance, and all other actions we have talked about in this study are possible apart from a personal relationship with God?
- Looking again at John, read the context of what Jesus told his disciples in John 15:1-5. Are you abiding in Christ and is Christ abiding in you? Or are you "apart" from Him? A simple way of thinking about this is the word picture Jesus uses: we are either branches that are receiving life from the vine they are connected to (Jesus), or we are branches that are separated and withering. All of us need to grapple with Jesus' claim that apart from Him we can do nothing. Tim Keller put it well: "The gospel [the good news] is this: We are more sinful and flawed in ourselves than we ever dared believe, yet at the very same time we are more loved and accepted in Jesus Christ than we ever dared hope."[3]

[3] Keller, T. (2011). *The meaning of marriage : facing the complexities of commitment with the wisdom of God*. New York: Dutton. p. 44.

- Have you ever accepted Jesus' freely offered love and decided to trust Him and follow Him? If not, please consider His offer; He is longing for you to accept Him! One good place to learn more about His invitation is at cru.org, at the link, "How to Know God."

Then, consider:

- How might accepting Jesus' offer transform your life and your marriage?
- Are you willing to say yes to God's invitation? It can be a prayer as simple as this: "Jesus, I have tried to live for myself. Forgive me. I need You. I don't want to be separated from You and Your love. I give You my life. I choose to trust You and follow You. Please live in me, and help me to live in You." If you are willing, open your heart to God now and accept His invitation.
- If you have made that decision and have accepted Christ's invitation, welcome to the family of God!! We are so thrilled to be a part of your life and journey!

As you move forward, we encourage you to make your faith commitment lasting, abiding and real in your life by taking some next steps. First, share your decision with someone, who can begin to support you and help you grow in your faith. (Your spouse, a trusted friend, a pastor …) Then if you haven't already, plug in to a local church and Christian community. And keep your heart trusting and open to the One who will always be there for you, guiding you in your marriage, your life, and your eternity.

notes

Access the teaching videos (Free)

Unlocking an Intimate Marriage includes 8 sessions of video teaching that leads the discussion times detailed in this study.

You can access the videos at two locations:

1) *Through* rightnow MEDIA

If you or your church have an account with rightnow MEDIA, you can access the videos through your account. Find the link on UnlockinganIntiateMarriage.com.

2) *Hosted by Building Intimate Marriages, Inc.*

Through Building Intimate Marriages, Inc you can access all 8 teaching sessions for free if you don't have a rightnow MEDIA account.

A) Go to: UnlockinganIntimateMarriage.com/videos

B) Scroll down and select "Let's Start" ($39.99 option)

C) Under "Order Summary", click "Add Coupon Code"

D) **Enter coupon code:** UIMGUIDE and select "Apply"

E) You can now register for *free* to watch the teaching videos.

Read the book that goes with the study!

Want to **communicate** better, *grow together,* and continue to build a more *intimate marriage?*

Read the book out loud to one another, and get ready for even more *"aha moments!"*

SHAUNTI FELDHAHN & DR. MICHAEL SYTSMA

secrets of sex & marriag

8 Surprises That Ma All the Difference

"I highly recommend this insightful book
—Gary Chapman, PhD, author of The 5 Love Lan

66 I highly recommend this insightful book to all married couples. 99

- Gary Chapman, PhD
Author of *The 5 Love Languages*

66 A book like this only comes around every so many decades. As therapists who work with minority populations, we cannot be more excited to share such a transformational tool. 99

- Jorge and Danisa Suarez,
Marriage counselors and sex therapists;
Co-hosts of SexoDivino TV

Made in the USA
Las Vegas, NV
14 September 2024

95244815R00056